Interior layout by Joey Aldridge
Cover design by Rhonda L McIntosh- Tipton

Important notice for all readers of this series!

This book is dedicated to two very special people:

My dear Mum who passed away after a brave fight against pancreatic cancer. She was my biggest fan and loved to read about my zany forest realm characters.

Brenda Delysia Aldridge
27th October 1947 – 9th November 2022

I love you dearly, Mum, and my heart breaks every morning when I wake up and remember that you are no longer with us.

In memory and in honour of this courageous lady, for any stories written after this book the main character of Anita will be replaced by a new character:

Brendelysia

My darling big sister, Honey Michelle Almazar who is now also facing a battle against cancer. You are strong, you are brave, but most of all you are not alone, Sis. We stand together, no matter how physically far apart we may be.

Acknowledgements:
Much love and thanks go to the following people...

Our dear Dad, who lost his soulmate of fifty-five years. Despite his own grief he still has the strength to comfort both his daughters.
Our beloved cousin, Jane MacAulay and her husband Jim, for all their support and love during a tragic time.

Sarah MacAulay, Paula & Tonia, Ian and Lynne Masson, U'Llynda-Jaye, Dominic, Maddison, Devvyn, Trent and Graham – dearest cousins whose support we have cherished.

To Giselle and Josephine, Mum's younger sisters – the best aunts a person could ask for.

Pamela Welch – the best Mum-in-Law a person could ask for.

Charlie "Big Bro" Almazar –The best Bro-in-Law a person could ask for.

Karen Welch – the best Sister-in-Law a person could ask for.

For all members of our family in this time of grief.

And to the following dear friends a.k.a. our extended family:

Will Walton

David Minihane
Kirstie Baudains
Martin Baxter
Bethany Salsac
Clare Fotheringham
Penny Mitchem
Claire Daws
I am so grateful for your kindness
and understanding.

Tales From the Forest:
Some Like It Hot!
A Short Story
Or "It's Called Extreme Sports for a Reason"

By Johanna Sarah Aldridge

Dearest Reader.

Anita the Forest Witch here. As you have just read in the Author's dedications above, I will be leaving the Forest Realm and returning to my family, whom I have not seen in a long time and have missed so much.

I hereby tender my resignation as Forest Witch and Caretaker of the Forest Realm, and wish my successor, Brendelysia, all the best in her new life.

In the meantime, I just HAD to share this little anecdote with you all before I sign off for good.

My dear little friends, the garden snails, Salad and Bertram, have been up to mischief again.

You may recall their little adventure in the first book of Tales From the Forest?

I love them both to bits, but oh mercy Mother Moon!

This one really takes... the chilli!

It all began one Sunday afternoon when two bored garden snails decided to have another race.

Some might question the wisdom of this especially given the trouble they caused in the Forest Witch's Garden the first time we met them.

Ever determined and with the enthusiasm of Olympic champions, the two friends *very slowly* made up their minds.

But one may ask, how did they reach this place? Well?

The conversation went something like this...

"Oh man I'm hungry!" Salad whined aloud. "What we want for lunch, ma snail?"
Bertram pondered that for a long, long, longgggg moment.

"Well," he said, thirty minutes later. "D'em big red, long t'ings over d'ere look good, man."

Salad slowly turned his head to regard the 'big red, long t'ings'.

"Pretty! Sound good to me man!" He frowned suddenly. "Where we at anyways, ma snail?"

Bertram frowned, deep in thought. Ten minutes later he shrugged, an action that took a further five minutes to execute.

"Me tinkin' we in da Forest, man!" he announced triumphantly.

Salad surveyed the area, antennae slowly swinging back and forth. "True dat! Race ya!"

"Man, you got no chance!"
"I'm da fastest snail in da Forest Realm, ma man!"

"You yankin' ma foot, snail? No *wayyyyy!*"

Bickering, and occasionally forgetting what they were supposed to be doing, they set off in the direction of the 'big red long t'ings'.

So fixed on their objective, and busy trying to best each other, neither snail noticed the sign along the way:

Stay away from the Chillies.
Not fit for consumption.
For Potent Magika only

Had they been able to read it they might have thought twice about their race (though this would have taken much more time and made this story ridiculously long).

They also might have noticed that they were in the Forest Witch's Garden and they were heading to the one area that *everyone* was expressly forbidden from, and for good reason.

Later that day...

Much had been on her mind of late. So much that it felt as though her head might explode. She'd needed time to think things through before any decisions could be made, but now that time was done.

Anita had made up her mind. She missed her home in the human world, her parents, her siblings... it was time to leave the Forest Realm.

Should she say all this out loud?

No. Not today. It was too nice out here and she just wanted to think about something else for once. Maybe she wouldn't say anything. Just disappear off into the night...

"Such a lovely day," Anita announced aloud, deliberately breaking that train of thought. "And that swim in the river this morning was just what I needed to relax."

She was sitting in her best friend's garden with its nice big lawn and flourishing plant life. Sophia, a young she-wolf with an absentminded genius-magic user for a husband and four adventurous pups that kept her on her paws morning, noon, and night, had nonetheless managed to find the time to really make this place into a home.

The cave entrance was adorned with hanging baskets of fragrant blue and red flowers, a doorbell of all things, and even a large shaggy green welcome mat on the veranda that proclaimed, with no hint of irony:

All are welcome to enter our home.
Please remove shoes before entering.
Clean up your own mess and, above all,
be nice...
We are werewolves, after all.

Peace be your friend on the journey home

That had to be Devlin, Sophia's husband, Anita mused silently and grinned. It was his idea of a friendly warning, but most of the Forest's residents knew this pack wouldn't harm a fly.

She took a long, slow breath and tipped her head back, relaxing her muscles and drinking in the sunlight.

It was so nice, sitting and listening to the Forest, knowing that all essential chores had been completed, and it was now time to spend a few days just chilling out with her friend, like a sort of mini break. Even Bonnie Blackbird was singing happily as she fed from the bird table; then there was the relaxing sound of a stream merrily babbling away nearby, the scent of wild honeysuckle so sweet and pleasant on the summer breeze...

Sophia suddenly sat up and cocked her head to one side. "You hear that?"
Anita placed her mug of tea back on the garden table and listened carefully.
"Only thing I can hear is snoring," she murmured in dry amusement.

Both women glanced over at two wolf pups sprawled in the grass, paws up, tongues lolling out, and tails beating ever so slightly, indicating that whatever they were dreaming about they were having fun. Ben and Jamie had been play-fighting in the river most of the morning, and once they'd bolted down their lunch at a rate that made Anita's eyes water they'd fallen into a post-prandial doze. Ben, perhaps because he was the oldest and the biggest, snored much louder than his little brother with the occasional pig-like snort thrown in for good measure.

Anita smiled fondly when the little red wolf rolled over in his sleep until his back was right up against his big brother, who at the same time rolled over until Jamie was tucked securely up against his chest and belly.

"They can be almost unbearably cute at times, eh?" Sophia remarked with a small chuckle, then her expression snapped to something more serious. "There it goes again! What on earth is it? It's really bugging me now..."

She got up and stalked to the garden gate, frowning, and glancing up and down along the forest path.

The witch raised an eyebrow. Werewolf hearing was extraordinary and no doubt whatever Sophia was picking up on was still miles away right at that moment. Surely, it would be some time before Anita heard it.

"What's it sound like?" she asked, curiously.

Sophia carried on looking out into the forest. "Like someone screaming in fear, or pain." she thought about it for a second. "Or both."

Immediately concerned, Anita's eyes narrowed. "Where are the girls?"

"Oh, they went with their father to visit the Rat Sanctuary up in the mountains," Sophia replied. "Laura was concerned about a rash Martin had picked up in some embarrassing place. They thought it would be a laugh, though I suspect it's more likely to give them nightmares. They should be back by tomorrow evening."

A loud sneeze attracted their attention, followed by Ben crying out "Cor blimey! Something don't half pong!"

Jamie, also rudely awakened, was pawing frantically at his nose. "Agh! Ben! Can't breathe!"

Ben immediately morphed into his human form and scooped the red wolf pup into his arms. "Seriously, Mum! Ease off on the vindaloos, would ya? I know you like curry but maybe next time have a Korma for once!"

With that, the young wolf turned his back and marched off into the cave, rubbing Jamie's belly and crooning reassurances.

Sophia's nose twitched. "Ben's right!" she glanced at her friend. "Not about the curry, but... can't you smell that yet?"

Anita shook her bewildered. "My sense of smell and hearing isn't as good as yours, I'm afraid."

And then, suddenly, Anita could hear it. A long, drawn-out scream that grew louder and louder each second that passed.

"...oooooaaarrrgghhhhhhHHHARRRRGGHHHHHH ..."

Anita squinted into the distance and spied movement along the forest path.

"Whatever it is, it's getting closer."

Indeed, it was, because now the werewolf and witch could make out garbled words in the screaming.

"Look, there!" Anita exclaimed and pointed out a fast-moving shape blazing its way towards them and kicking up a dense trail of dust in its wake. The ground caught fire briefly as the object passed by, before safely fizzling out and leaving deep scorch marks on the path.

Before she could worry about fire hazards, the screamed, garbled words became clearer.

"...Hot!Hot!Hot!Ow!Ow!Ow!Hurts!Hurts!Hurts!Id on'tlikeit!Idon'tlike it!Idon'tlikeitttttt!!!!Helppppp!!!"

As it zipped past Sophia's garden gate, accompanied by the sound normally associated with someone on a high-fibre baked-bean diet, the force of the slip stream knocked the werewolf and witch off their feet. Too shocked to save themselves, they both landed hard on their bums and groaned in pain.

Ego more bruised than her derriere, Sophia shot to her feet again.

"What in *blazes* was that?!" she hissed, angrily.

Then she made the mistake of taking in a deep breath and began to splutter indignantly.

"Ugh! Someone help me!" Sophia's eyes were watering terribly by now. "What *is* that smell? It's rank! There are sewers in the city that smell better than this!"

Judging by the look on her face, the Forest Witch had already figured it out.

"That, my friend is the result of someone binging on my special new hot chillies," Anita puffed out a breath, still rubbing her bottom and scowling deeply. "They're not supposed to be eaten, just for use in my new supersonic broomstick recipe. Because of the side effect that I've not been able to cure, I call it The Hot Fart."

She considered the situation for a very short moment, then announced: "I'd sit down again if I were you."

Sophia frowned. "What? Why?"

"Because I know who else is coming!" The witch grabbed her friend's arm and pulled her back down onto the grass. "Wait for it..."

There came a blast of noise, dust and what could only be described as a *fart* scorched another trail past the garden.

The two friends sat there listening and trying hard not to breathe, while the screaming gradually died down as the phenomena careened further away into the forest.

Unfortunately, the smell was taking it's less than sweet time about joining it.

When it eventually became safe to breathe without a cloth over their mouths, Sophia turned to the witch.

"The Hot Fart?" at Anita's nod, Sophia blew out a breath. "Please explain."

Anita sighed. "You've heard of the Carolina Reaper Chilli?" When the werewolf nodded, she continued. "Well, times it's heat by about... ooh... twenty..."

"Twenty?" Sophia interrupted, a tad scornfully, known throughout the realm as an expert chilli eater. "That's nothing..."

"... thousand." Anita grinned, smugly. "Those screaming streaks you just saw? That was Bertram and Salad."

Sophia's frown dissolved as apprehension dawned. She grinned, wolfishly. "Your garden snails? Oh dear."

Whereas Anita's grin now matched that of a shark. "Oh dear, indeed."

* * *

Two hours later, Anita and Sophia were standing in Anita's garden, towering in pretend anger over the two snails.

"Ohhhh man!" Salad wailed, mournfully. "Ma backside is still on *fire* ma snail!"

Bertram looked just as pained. "Never again, ma witch, we promise, as The Forest is our witness!" Salad huffed a little, looking dejected. "But t'ankyou for d'ice."

The two snails were each perched on ice cubes that had only been magiked into existence a few seconds ago but were already melting. Steam rose around them, and a sizzling noise could be heard, rather like bacon frying in a pan of hot oil.

"Well," said Anita, and sniffed, sticking her nose in the air. "Perhaps that will teach you to mess with the forbidden area of the garden. I mean, didn't you read the warning sign? Those chillies were an experimental ingredient in a spell to make broomsticks fly faster!"

The two snails glanced at each other.

"What sign, ma witch?" said Bertram, cautiously. "We saw no sign."

"And even if we did, snails can't *read* man!" Salad added.

"Let it be a lesson to you at any rate," said Anita, making a mental note to look up a spell that would allow the snails to read. "Do NOT go into the forbidden area of the garden. You could've set the entire forest on fire!"

The snails looked confused, and Anita sighed.

"Eating Chillies is NOT, repeat, NOT an extreme sport!"

"You're on ma witch." replied Bertram, shamefully.

"Sorry ma lady." said Salad, staring down at the ground.

Anita eyed them carefully, and then nodded. "Alright then. You may go."

* * *

Another two days passed by in peace and quiet, but it seemed their little experiment wasn't over...

"You'd really think they would've learned their lesson by now, eh?" asked Sophia, amused.

Anita offered up a helpless smile. "Not in the slightest."

They peered through the slit in the curtain and there was Bertram and Salad, slithering their way over to the chillies once more.

The witch and werewolf could just about make out their conversation.

"Oh man, it hurt, but it were *good!*"

"Right *on* ma snail! We *never* moved d'at fast before... *ever*."

Or maybe they *had* learned something, Anita thought, as she looked them over.

This time the snails were sporting safety helmets, fire extinguishers, and each carried a bottle of Anita's special Aloe Vera Burn Cream hanging on a piece of string around their necks.

"They might be slow," said Anita, trying not to laugh as she magiked up another bowl of ice. "But they ain't stupid."

* * *

Anita and Sophia hurried through the forest after the snails, not that their trail was exactly hard to follow. There were the scorch marks, for one thing. For another there was the smell — with her acute werewolf nose, poor Sophia was almost in physical pain from it! — and if that wasn't enough, the whole forest must have been able to hear the screams as the two shelled-idiots rocketed through the undergrowth...

"AHHHHGGGHHHHHHHHH…FIRE IN'DA HOLE!!!!!!!!!!!"

Anita inclined her head slightly in consideration.

"Well, that's one way of putting it," she said with a sniff, and immediately regretted it as her nose began to turn red and it felt as though her nostril hairs were on fire.

Sophia chuckled despite the pain she herself was in.

"Come on," said the She-Wolf, and linked arms with the witch. "Let's go see what's left of them."

But as they approached the brow of a hill, just before a clearing where Arthur the Stag often grazed, it became immediately apparent that something else was going on.

There came loud whispering, and a series of *'shhhhhh's* which fell silent as the two women appeared.

Anita frowned, instantly suspicious.

There was no one there. Not a soul. Just the scorch marks that cut off abruptly at the edge of the clearing in a puddle of fresh mud and water.

The witch and the werewolf exchanged glances and nodded.

"Alright!" Anita called out, hands on hips and an expression on her face that dared anyone to mess with her. "What's going on? Sophia can smell you all so there's no point in hiding!"

What happened next was completely unexpected.

Dozens of squirrels, rabbits, including Billy Bunny, Nelson the Black Lab, Arthur the Stag and all his kin, Mr and Mrs Robin, the mice family that lived in Anita's cottage, Reynard the Fox, Sophia's mate Devlin and their four pups, the Frost Elves, the Sun Elves, Felicia the bear and her family, the Otters, and a whole host of other Forest Realm inhabitants, all crept out from behind various trees, bushes, and rocks, grinning sheepishly. And right at the front, of course, were the two snails guarding a large cake that bulged with raspberry jam and cream, and written clumsily in frosted icing on the top was the legend:

Good luck Anita!

We love you!

Anita blinked then turned to look at her friend, who was smiling softly back at her.

"You must've known we weren't going to let you leave without saying goodbye," said Sophia, sadly.

After a few false starts, Anita managed to speak again.

"How did you know?" she asked, voice husky and raw from unshed tears. She thought she'd been so clever and secretive, preparing for the long journey ahead as quietly as possible. She hated farewells. They may be sweet, but they were also private, painful, and emotional, especially when she knew it was final – she would never return to this realm.

A rustle in the branches above her head signified the arrival of one last member of Anita's extended family.

"Aunty Owl," she said, and exhaled sharply. "I should have realised."

"Too right my gal!" came the expected fond but disgruntled reply.

Another rustle and the big owl landed gently on Anita's outstretched arm.

"I could tell something was weighing heavily on you, but it wasn't until I saw you packing late one night that I knew what you had to do." Aunty stared deep into Anita's eyes. "It's ok to go home. You're ready. Just remember that wherever you are, so will we be. All you have to do is think of us."

"Oh, Mercy Mother Moon!" Anita sniffed, as tears cascaded down her face. "I was hoping to avoid this! I *hate* crying!"

"It's ok to cry," said Aunty, with a soft smile as the Forest Realm animals gathered around their friend to whisper their own messages of love and support.

And so, we leave them to their farewell party, because as Anita quite rightly pointed out: *farewells are painful.*

The End.

Many thanks for reading, hope you all enjoyed it.
If you would like to know more about our dog sanctuary project and any other works in progress, please feel free to find me here:

Website: johannaaldridge.com

Facebook: @dogdayssanctuary

Twitter: @puppydogtales74

Always yours,

Joey Aldridge

Other books in the Forest Realm series:
Book One: Short Stories, Long Friendships

All proceeds to our sanctuary for stray, elderly, and abandoned dogs
Book Two in the Forest Realm Series: Sea the Light
All proceeds go to the British Heart Foundation in memory of my dear friend Justin "Buster" Brown.

Tales from the Forest: Anita's Book of Songspells and other thoughtful poetry

Author's Biography

Jo was born in the former Roman town of Colchester in Essex, England in the year 1974. She attended East Bergholt Primary and, later, East Bergholt High School.

She was not considered to be a particularly bright student and was often ridiculed by classmates and teachers alike. No one expected her to gain double As in GCSE science, or a B in Craft Design and Technology. She was the only girl in her year to take up Computer Literacy during the 'options' year, and went on to score an R.S.A distinction. Her A Levels were a bit of a flop, but she did well in her Air Training Corps exams, and she went on to become 1334 Manningtree Squadron's first female Staff Cadet, and first female Cadet Warrant Officer. During her summer and Christmas holidays, she went to work on the apple farm with her father, and spent almost every night sitting round the campfire in her parent's garden gazing up at the stars or watching the owls as her father called to them with his Owl Hoot.

As it happened, although she missed getting into Essex University due to her bad A Level results, in 1992 she was accepted by Anglia Ruskin University in Cambridge. So, she went off to Cambridgeshire where she obtained a BSc with honours in Cell and Molecular Biology. Not able to find work because she was too young and too inexperienced, Jo went back to work as a part-time labourer on the fruit farm. She performed a variety of tasks but her personal favourite was budding and grafting, which was, she felt, at least a little closer to the science she had studied! After a summer on the farm, it was pointed out to her that she could get a bursary for studying a PGCE in secondary school science. It wasn't much at the time, but she reasoned that it was 'better than a poke in the eye with a sharp stick,' which, incidentally, was exactly what she had recently suffered when a colleague accidentally let go of a rather springy apple branch... So, in 1995, she packed up and went to live in Southend, Essex, while she studied for a Post Graduate Certificate in Education. Following a few teaching stints at various schools, she obtained her teaching qualification. However, after realising that she missed having a social life, rather than a life that seemed solely based on marking test papers, she decided to ditch teaching high school science and go into the clinical laboratory sciences. In 1997, she started work as a Medical Laboratory Assistant at Ipswich Hospital in Suffolk, and by the end of 1998 she had finished her training as a Biomedical Scientist, specialising in Clinical Biochemistry. In 2001, she decided to move on and took another post as a biomedical scientist, this time somewhere completely different... so, she moved to Jersey, the largest of the Channel Islands just off the North Coast of France. In 2005 she became a Fellow of the Institute of Biomedical Science, a full Member of the Royal Society of Biology, and a Chartered Biologist. After 14 years of waiting for Jo, her best friend Scott proposed and she finally said yes. In 2006, her fiancé, Scott, moved to Jersey, and they got married at the very lovely Elizabeth Castle surrounded by friends and family who had travelled from as far away as Australia to be there. In 2010, a tiny black Labrador puppy came to their house and life was never the same again. That puppy grew into a cheeky chappy, with big, soft, floppy ears, one of the longest tongues you'll ever see, and the usual rapacious appetite that often leaves Labrador owners in despair whenever the next check-up at the vets is due. In all this time, Jo has secretly enjoyed writing fiction and non-fiction stories, as well as the odd poem, for her own amusement. Her guilty pleasure is writing fan fiction stories for the Supernatural fandom, but mostly she uses creative writing as self-directed therapy when life becomes too overwhelming. After ten years of writing fan fiction, her long-suffering husband eventually told her it was about time she had something published. And so here she is... a published author.

Printed in Great Britain
by Amazon

18392773R00025